Language Patterns

Language Patterns
Series Information

READINESS

KATE & FLUFFY BOOKS   Age 5/6

Teacher's Handbook   ISBN 0-03-910204-1

Complete Set of 5 × 10 titles   ISBN 0-03-910203-3

STORY METHOD BOOKS   Age 5/6

Teacher's Resource Book Readiness to Stage 3
ISBN 0-03-910201-7

Complete Set of 5 × 10 titles   ISBN 0-03-910234-3

STAGE I   Age 5/6

Animal Friends   ISBN 0-03-910235-1

It's Fun   ISBN 0-03-910236-X

It's Magic   ISBN 0-03-910237-8

Happy Ever After   ISBN 0-03-910238-6

Working with Letters 1   ISBN 0-03-910200-9

Working with Letters 2   ISBN 0-03-910239-4

Working with Letters 3   ISBN 0-03-910240-8

Tracing our Letters   ISBN 0-03-910317-X

STAGE 2   Age 6/7

Tiny Tails   ISBN 0-03-910241-6

Animals from Everywhere   ISBN 0-03-910242-4

Step by Step   ISBN 0-03-910243-2

Stories Old and New   ISBN 0-03-910244-0

Words and Meaning 1   ISBN 0-03-910245-9

Spelling Book 1   ISBN 0-03-910246-7

Thinking and Writing 1   ISBN 0-03-910247-5

STAGE 3   Age 7/8

Believe It or Not   ISBN 0-03-910248-3

Here and There   ISBN 0-03-910249-1

Words and Meaning 2   ISBN 0-03-910250-5

Spelling Book 2   ISBN 0-03-910251-3

Thinking and Writing 2   ISBN 0-03-910252-1

Animal Friends

Editor: **Donald Moyle**   Associate Editor: **James Bromley**

Linguistics Consultant: Peter Parry

HOLT, RINEHART AND WINSTON

Copyright © 1981 by Holt, Rinehart and Winston Ltd.
ISBN 0–03–910235–1

Language Patterns Stage 1

Readers   **Workbooks**

1. **Animal Friends** ⟶ **Working With Letters Book 1** ⎫
2. **It's Fun** ⟶ **Working With Letters Book 2** ⎬ **Language Skills**
3. **It's Magic** ⎫ ⟶ **Working with Letters Book 3** ⎭
4. **Happy ever after** ⎭

Apparatus
Tracing our letters – flocked alphabet cards

For teacher
Resource book for Stage 1 to 3

ACKNOWLEDGEMENTS

Care has been exercised to trace ownership of copyright material contained in this text. The publishers will gladly receive information that will enable them to rectify any reference or credit in subsequent editions.

Cover Design: MARY MURPHY   *Book Design:* TOM SANKEY

Illustrators:

BARRIE APPLEBY   SUSANNE DOLESCH
RUTH BAGSHAW   JANE H. GOTTARDI
PHILIP BALSAM   GORDON RAYNER, SR.
KALMAN BANITZ   TOM SANKEY
RALPH G. CAMPBELL   BOB SEGUIN
ALAN DANIEL   J. MERLE SMITH
CHARLES DOLESCH   NATIONAL FILM BOARD OF CANADA
                        EDWARD TAYLOR

It is illegal to reproduce any portion of this book except by special arrangement with the publishers. Reproduction of this material without authorization by any duplication process whatsoever is a violation of copyright.

Animal Friends is based on Listening Letters (Linn, Bruce, Donaldson, Ellis, Saunders, Trischuk) from Language Patterns © by Holt, Rinehart and Winston of Canada, Limited

Printed in Great Britain by Ebenezer Baylis & Son Ltd, The Trinity Press, Worcester, and London.
Print Number: 9 8 7 6 5 4 3 2 1

Contents

Sam

Sam is a dog.

"Sam, Sam,
sit, Sam."

Sam sits.

Tim

Tim is a boy.

This is Tim.

Tim sits.

Sam is a dog.

This is Sam.

Sam is Tim's dog.

Tim sits and Sam sits.

The postman has a parcel.

Is the parcel for Tim?

Yes it is!

The parcel is for Tim.

It is a bat for Tim.

Batting

Tim is batting.

"Hit the ball Tim."

Tim hits the ball.

Jim is batting.

"Hit the ball Jim!

Hit it Jim."

Jim hits the ball.

John is batting

"Hit the ball John!

Hit it!"

John hits the ball.

Sam has the bat.

Is Sam batting?

Can Sam hit the ball?

Tip's Bad Habit

Tip is a bad dog.

This is Tip.

Tip has a bad habit.

This is his bad habit.

He is a jam licker.

Pam sees Tip licking the jam.

She stamps.

Tip jumps back.

The jam tips.

Plop!

The jam hits the mat.

Tip tips up.

He falls in the jam on the mat.

Jammy Tip has a bath.

Mac the Rat

This is Miss Smith.

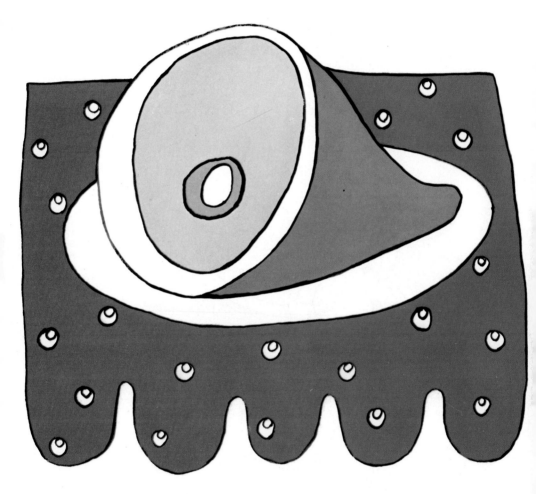

This is a ham.

It is Miss Smith's ham.

Mac the Rat likes ham.

Mac bit Miss Smith's ham.

Miss Smith's ham is good.

Miss Smith looks at the ham.

She thinks, "That rat.

That rat has bit the ham."

Miss Smith has a trap.

The trap has ham in it.

Miss Smith's ham.

Mac is by the trap.

He hits the trap. Bang!

Mac has the ham.

Miss Smith's ham.

Mac thinks, "This is good ham."

Can you tell a story please?

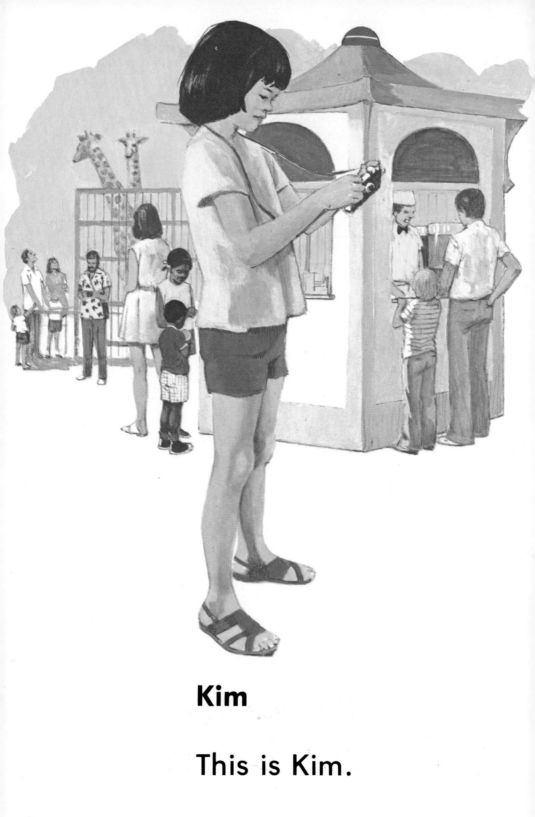

Kim

This is Kim.

This is a tiger.

He lives at the zoo.

The keeper is with the tiger.

He has some meat.

The tiger snaps at the meat.

Click, Kim snaps the tiger.

Click, she snaps the man.

The tiger sees Kim.

He snaps at Kim.

The T.P.

This is Tim.

He has a hat.

This is Pat.

Sam the dog

is with them.

This is the T.P.

The T.P. is a raft.

It is Tim's and Pat's.

Tim, Pat and Sam

are on the raft.

Tim has jam to eat.

Pat has ham to eat.

Sam is tired. He has a nap.

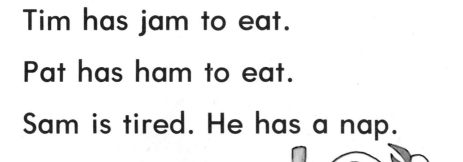

Tim sits by the mast.

Pat sits by the mast.

Sam naps.

The T.P. tips up.

Tim falls on Pat.

Pat falls on Sam.

Tim, Pat and Sam fall

in the water.

Pat has a bath.

Tim has a bath

and Sam has a bath.

Can you tell a story please?

Kip

Kip is a white dog.

He is at camp.

He sits in the path
and traps rabbits.

Kip sits by the trap.

The trap is in the path.

Kip naps.

Can he trap the rabbit?

An ant is on the path.

Kip has a nap.

The ant nips Kip.

Kip is inside.

He has a nap.

Kip cannot sit on the path.

Kip cannot sit on the floor.

He cannot sit!

The ant nipped Kip.

Tim and Ann

Tim jumps up onto a wall.

He says, "Look I am tall

And you are small."

Ann says, "Please be careful

not to fall."

Tim skips along the wall

Singing, "Look I am tall

And you are small.

I am going to bounce my ball."

Tim skips and jumps.

He bounces his ball.

But now he falls off the wall.

He feels his lumps and bumps.

But Ann says, "Now I am tall

and you are small."

Spin, Top, Spin

Ron has a top.

Ron's top spins.

Spin top spin.

Spin on the spot.

Stop, top, stop.

Stop, stop, stop.

Tom Kicks

This is Ann.

Ann is a girl.

This is Tom.

Tom is a horse.

Ann sits on Tom.

Tom trots on the path.

Ann sits on Tom as he trots.

There is a rabbit in the grass.

It hops across the path.

Tom kicks.

Ann falls off Tom.

Ann is not on Tom.

She hits a rock.

She sobs.

Ann's back hurts.

Ann is on a bed.

Mum rubs Ann's back.

Ann thanks Mum.

Bob's Pig

This is Bob.

Bob is a boy.

Bob has a pig.

It is not a big pig.

It is a little pig.

Bob has a sack.

He has carrots in his sack.

The pig grabs a carrot.

Bob thinks, "That pig is

not a pig. It is a hog."

Bob sits by the rock.

His sack is on the grass.

Bob has a nap.

The pig grabs the bag.

He has a snack.

Then the pig naps on the grass.